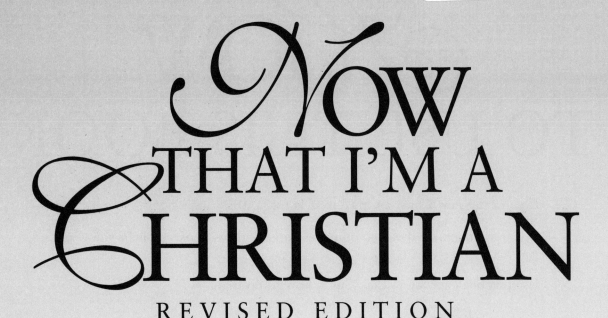

Now
THAT I'M A
CHRISTIAN

REVISED EDITION

WILLIAM E. YOUNG

A book for children who are new Christians to be used at
home with guidance and encouragement
of a parent or other adult.

Convention Press
Nashville, Tennessee

$\mathcal{H}OW$
TO USE THIS BOOK

If you are a new Christian, this book is for you.

If you are thinking about becoming a Christian, this book can help you.

Use this book for six weeks. This is how to do that.

 • This book is to be used at home.

 • There is a page for each day—Monday, Tuesday, Wednesday, and Thursday. Use the pages for Fridays to think back over what you have studied that week.

• Prayer thoughts can help you pray each day.

 • Get ready for church on Saturdays.

 • Go to church on Sundays.

• Set aside a special time and place to use this book.

 • Ask an adult to help you read and think through each day's material. Being with an adult who cares about you can be a meaningful time. Ask about any word, idea, or teaching you do not understand. Let the adult help you.

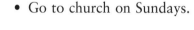 • When you finish the book, get the certificate signed.

CONTENTS

© Copyright 1996 Convention Press *All rights reserved* Nashville, Tennessee

ISBN # 0-7673-2040-9

Dewey Decimal Classification Number: J248.82

Subject Heading: CHILDREN—RELIGIOUS LIFE

Children/Preschool Section

Youth/Children/Preschool Department

Discipleship and Family Group

LifeWay Church Resources

LifeWay Christian Resources of the Southern Baptist Convention

127 Ninth Avenue, North, Nashville, Tennessee 37234

All Scripture references are from the Holy Bible, New International Version, copyright © 1973, 1978, 1984 by
International Bible Society. Used by permission.

We believe that the Bible has God for its author; salvation for its end; and truth, without any mixture of error, for its
matter and that all Scripture is totally true and trustworthy. The 2000 statement of *The Baptist Faith and Message* is
our doctrinal guide.

What Does the New Testament Say Makes a Person a Christian?

Bible verse: "For God so loved the world that he gave his one and only Son, that whoever believes in him shall not perish but have eternal life" *(John 3:16).*

Place a circle around *believe* and all of the words that mean *to believe* in the paragraph below.

To become a Christian, a person must believe that Jesus can and will save him or her. To *believe* in Jesus means to trust Him to save. A person who trusts in Jesus will want to turn away from sin as a way of living. He will want to please God instead of himself.

Place a rectangle around the word *following* and all of the words that mean *to follow* Jesus in the paragraphs below.

Following Jesus means being willing to do whatever Jesus asks. Deciding to follow Jesus is a promise for all of your life.

A person who wants to become a Christian must trust in Jesus for himself. No one else can do that for him. He must know who Jesus is and what Jesus has done for him. He must decide to trust Jesus to save him.

In the following stories, place a check mark (✓) every place that you read where a person *believes* or *follows.*

Paul

I am Paul. I was a Jewish leader. At first, I thought Christians were enemies of my religion.

One day, I was traveling to arrest Christians in Damascus. I saw a great light. A voice said, "Why are you persecuting Me?"

I said, "Who are You, Lord?"

The voice said, "I am Jesus."

The Christians were right. Jesus is the Savior the prophets wrote about. And Jesus is not dead but alive, as the Christians said.

That day my life changed. I only want to tell everyone who Jesus is.

—Based on Acts 9:1-22

The Ethiopian

I was the treasurer for the queen of the Ethiopians. I had been in Jerusalem to worship. On the way back, I was reading from a scroll of Isaiah's writings.

Philip, a Christian deacon, joined me and asked, "Do you understand what you are reading?"

"How can I unless someone helps me?" I answered. Then I asked him to sit in the chariot with me.

Philip told me about Jesus. He said Jesus was the one Isaiah had written about. Jesus had given His life on the cross for me and my sin. And Jesus had risen from the dead.

When we came to some water, I asked Philip to baptize me.

—Based on Acts 8:26-39

Finish this sentence. To become a Christian a person must _____

_____

_____

Pray. Thank God for making it possible for you to become a Christian.

5

Important
Words to Understand

Bible verse: "Believe in the Lord Jesus, and you will be saved" *(Acts 16:31).*

What *Believe* Means . . .

Believe means more than to know about Jesus. It means to trust.

Many persons say they believe in Jesus. Their minds know He is God's Son. They even say He died on the cross for the whole world. But even Judas who betrayed Jesus knew this was true. (Read James 2:19 to see who else believes this way.)

This kind of believing is not the same as trusting Jesus enough to turn your life over to Him.

Believe means to _____ Jesus.

What *Sin* Is . . .

God has given every person the right to choose. You can choose to obey God and His way, or you can please yourself. Sin is choosing to follow your way instead of God's. It is putting what you want above what God wants.

Sin is _____ to follow your way instead of God's.

The consequences of sin

The consequences of sin is separation from God. If we die without asking Jesus to be our Savior, we will spend eternity away from God.

In the paragraphs below circle the words that tell what God wants for people.

What *Being Saved* Means . . .

God is love. But God has to punish sin. In love, God has made a way to save people from the punishment they deserve. Jesus came to take the punishment for our sin.

To be saved means to be forgiven. It means to be back together with God forever. It means being adopted into God's family. Jesus died so that we could be saved.

What *Repent* Means . . .

To repent means to be so sorry for things you have done wrong. When you repent, you do not want to do the wrong things you did before. Repent also means turning to Jesus for forgiveness.

Think Time

What does it mean to trust someone?

Pray. Thank God for His Son, Jesus.

Jesus Must Come First

> *Bible verse:* "Jesus replied, 'If anyone loves me, he will obey my teaching'" *(John 14:23).*

A Christian Is . . .

A Christian is a believer in and a follower of Jesus Christ.

Who were called Christians?
"The disciples were called Christians first at Antioch" (Acts 11:26).

Jesus Is Lord

In Jesus' time, *lord* meant a master with power and the right to rule. To call Jesus "Lord" is very serious. Jesus even said so.

Jesus said, "Why do you call me 'Lord, Lord' and do not do what I say" (Luke 6:46). What does Jesus want those who call Him Lord to do? _____

_____

_____

You Can Choose

After you become a Christian, you still can choose to obey God or disobey Him. When you obey God, Jesus is being Lord of your life. When you disobey God, you (instead of Jesus) are being the lord of your life.

You choose to obey God because you love Him. You show God you love Him by doing the things that are right.

If Jesus Is First

If Jesus is first in your life, you will want to do what pleases Jesus.

1. List things you **do** when you let Jesus be Lord of your life.

2. List things you **do not do** when you let Jesus be Lord of your life.

Tell someone about some of the differences it makes when a person decides to let Jesus be his Lord—his master and ruler.

Pray. Ask God to help you put Jesus first in your life. Ask God to help you obey His commandments.

7

Becoming and Being a Christian

> *Bible verse:* "You are my friends if you do what I command" *(John 15:14).*

Becoming and Being

- There is a difference between becoming a Christian and being a Christian.
- You should be able to tell whether a person is a Christian.

What Is the Difference?

Being a Christian is something like taking a trip. It has a beginning, a middle, and a goal. As soon as a person trusts in Jesus Christ as her Savior, she becomes a Christian. That is like getting into the car to start the trip.

But getting into the car is not the whole trip. The same is true of being a Christian. Becoming a Christian is only the beginning. Being a Christian lasts a whole lifetime.

How to Be a Christian

Becoming a Christian is not a *job* that a person does for himself. It is God's work in him. The rest of a Christian's life is God's work, too.

God will keep on making a Christian more and more like Jesus as long as the Christian will let Him. But God will not force a Christian to act like a Christian.

- A Christian can choose to keep learning God's way—or he can quit studying. Read 2 Timothy 2:15.

- A Christian can try to think and act as Jesus would—or he can make excuses for acting like "everybody else."

But one thing is always true. A Christian will never be happy hiding his new life.

❏ What is the difference between becoming a Christian and being a Christian? _____
_____
_____

❏ What is the Christian's goal? _____
_____
_____

❏ In what ways did Jesus grow? Read Luke 2:52.
_____
_____

❏ What does Jesus expect Christians to do?
_____

❏ When a Christian sins, what should he do? Read 1 John 1:9.
_____
_____

List the ways you think you act like a Christian.
_____
_____
_____

Pray. Ask God to help you grow as Jesus grew.

Think Back

Right or Wrong?

These stories tell some people's ideas of how to become a Christian. If a story tells what you think is right, circle *YES*. Circle *NO* if you think the idea is wrong.

John's parents are Christians and members of the church near where they live. John says that being born into a Christian family makes him a Christian, too.

Is John a Christian because his parents are?

YES   NO

José goes to everything the church has for boys and girls. José can be counted on to be at church.

Does going to church meetings make José a Christian?

YES   NO

Mrs. Smith is always doing something for someone else. She helps prepare meals and helps a neighbor who is sick. She collects clothing for needy school children. She gives money to help people in need.

Do these good deeds make Mrs. Smith a Christian?

YES   NO

Brittany does not lie. Brittany is friendly, even to boys and girls others do not like. Teachers can trust Brittany to do what they ask. So can her parents.

Does being good make Brittany a Christian?

YES   NO

Mr. Gonzales spends time reading the Bible. He can say many Bible verses from memory.

Does reading the Bible make Mr. Gonzales a Christian?

YES   NO

Tom is nine. He wants to be a member of the church. He wants to be baptized.

Will being baptized and having his name on the church roll make Tom a Christian?

YES   NO

George has known for a long time what pleases his parents and other grown-ups. He also knows what things bring punishment.

One Sunday, George's pastor said that the Roman soldiers were wrong to kill Jesus. The soldiers knew that Jesus did not deserve to die. But those who put Him on the cross were no more guilty than we are. Jesus was dying for sin, and sin is a word for *I-want-my-own way.*

Not many weeks after that, when George was all alone, he made a decision. He asked God to forgive him for wanting his own way. George had decided to trust Jesus. He prayed, "I want Jesus to save me."

Is George a Christian?

YES   NO

Pray. Thank God for the Bible and for His plans for you to be saved.

9

God Is Great

Bible verse: "Great is the Lord and most worthy of praise" *(Psalm 145:3).*

This week you will learn about God—who He is and what He is like. You will not discover everything about Him. You never will. He is too great for that. But you can get to know God better and better through a whole lifetime.

How do you know God is great and powerful? "In the beginning God created . . ." (Genesis 1:1). Only a great God creates.

You Can Depend on God

God is dependable. Look at the world. Everywhere it shows you can depend on God.

Throw a ball up in the air and catch it. This act shows one of the laws God has set up for His world. It is the law of gravity. You can depend on that.

Trust is another word for depend. You can trust God.

God Has Always Been There

How great and powerful is God? Always there is God. "Lord, you have been our dwelling place throughout all generations. Before the mountains were born or you brought forth the earth and the world, from everlasting to everlasting you are God" (Psalm 90:1-2).

What does it mean to say, "God is great"?

Draw a picture of something that makes you think of God's greatness and power.

Pray. Thank Him for being a great God. Thank God for the Bible. Thank God for sending Jesus.

11

God Is Real

> *Bible verse:* "[Jesus said] Anyone who has seen me has seen the Father" *(John 14:9).*

God Is Spirit

You cannot tell just how God looks. The Bible says, "God is spirit" (John 4:24). This means that God does not have a body like you do. That is why you cannot see Him; no one has. But if God did have a body, He could be in only one place and do only one thing at a time. God is different from you.

God is different from you. You have to think of God in a different way. God is not just bigger and stronger. God is in a class all by Himself. For example, God can be everywhere and do all things. People cannot do this, but God can. He is Spirit.

You Can Know God Is Real

If you cannot see God and do not know how He looks, how can you be sure He is real?

For three reasons you can know God is real. The *first* is the wonderful world you live in. Only a powerful God, a real God could have created such a world. He is the always-dependable God.

The *second* is because of what you read in the Bible. There is the record of people for thousands of years who have believed in God. They knew Him and wrote of His wonderful works. They knew from experience that God is real.

The *third* and best reason for knowing God is real is His Son, Jesus. Jesus came to show how real God is and how much God understands and cares.

List three reasons you can know God is real.

_____

_____

_____

Pray. Thank God for helping you know Him better.

12

God Is Good

> *Bible verse:* "You are forgiving and good, O Lord, abounding in love to all who call to you" *(Psalm 86:5).*

God Always Does Right

One thing you know about God is that you are made in His image. Sometimes you do bad things. Does this mean God sometimes does bad things? No, God always does right.

Part of being made in God's image is having a mind and the right to choose. You can know right from wrong. And God lets you choose for yourself. You may choose wrong–but God never does.

God is all Good. Everything that is good begins with Him.

God Is Righteous (Does Right)

You may sometimes be mistaken, even unfair. But not God. God's laws are fair and right. He never makes a mistake. He treats everyone the same.

God Is Gracious

A person who is gracious is kind even when others do not deserve kindness. God is Gracious. That means He is good to us. He has even made a way to forgive you. You do not deserve such kindness from Him. What your sin deserves is punishment. But God is gracious to you.

God is Loving

The Bible tells us that He is a God of love. Psalm 23 says God is like a shepherd who loves and risks his life for his sheep.

Jesus said God is concerned even about sparrows. And every single person is much more important to God than a bird.

"Look at the birds of the air; they do not sow or reap or store away in barns, and yet your heavenly Father feeds them. Are you not much more valuable than they?" (Matthew 6:26).

What has God done for you?

Pray. Thank God for being good, doing right, and being kind.

13

God Is Our Father

> *Bible verse:* "The Spirit himself testifies with our spirit that we are God's children" *(Romans 8:16)*.

Jesus the Only Son of God

Jesus was God in a special way. Jesus was God coming to earth to help us understand who God is, and how He acts, and what He does. In John 14:9, find the words that say Jesus is God. "Anyone who has seen _____ has seen the _____."

People could look at Jesus and think, "God is like that." They saw Him loving all kinds of people, healing the sick, being kind to children, and forgiving His enemies.

Jesus called God His Father. He used that name when He talked with God in prayer. He used it when He decided to do all God wanted, even when it meant dying on the cross.

Jesus taught us how to be able to call God Father. He wants you to be able to call God Father. Jesus wants you to be as close to God as He is. He wants you to belong to God. That is why Jesus died for you.

The disciples wanted to know how to be this near to God. Jesus told them there was only one way. They understood what Jesus meant when He died and rose again.

God Our Father

Christians are "the children of God." We become children of God when we ask Jesus to be our Savior. All of the children of God put together make up the family of God. You are now a member of the family of God.

What Have You Learned?

• What does it mean to say that God is Father?

• When can a person honestly say, God is *my* Heavenly Father?

Place a check mark (✓) before each way that God is like a good father.

❑ He loves you

❑ He helps you

❑ He forgives you

❑ He is kind to you

Pray. Thank God that you know Him as your Heavenly Father.

┌────┐
│ 14 │
└────┘

Think Back

Who Is God?

All week you have been thinking about who God is and what He is like. Remember the things you have learned about God? Use the words in the box to fill in the blanks.

All good   great   real

- God is _____. He had no beginning, and He will be *forever*. He made all things. He can be trusted.
- God is _____. You cannot see Him because He is Spirit. He is a Person, not just an idea.
- God is ____ _____. He has never been un-fair or mistaken. He is love. He gave us Jesus.

For all these things and more, you can call our God *great*. But *great* is not the only way to de-scribe God. There is one word that tells best how He acts toward people.

The word—*Father*—tells these things about God:

- "Father" says He *made* people.

- "Father" says *Jesus* is God's *Son.*

- "Father" says *people* can *become* God's *children.*

The disciples wanted to know how to pray. They had seen Jesus praying; they had heard Him pray. They could tell how close God seemed when Jesus prayed. Jesus told them to talk to God like they would talk to a loving father (Matthew 6:5-15).

Use the words in the box to fill in the blanks below.

died   trusted   forever   Father

This is what calling God *Father* means to a Christian.

- I have _____ myself to Jesus.
- I know He _____ in my place.
- I know that God is my Heavenly _____.
- Someday I will live with Him _____.

How is God a loving Father to you?

You can still learn today from Jesus' stories–if you really want to. And there is a special secret about Jesus' stories. No matter how many times you hear one of them, it can still tell you some-thing new about God–if you really want to learn about God.

Can you match the Bible passages to the correct person from the list on the right?

(1) Luke 15:4-7   (a) a shepherd

(2) Luke 15:8-10   (b) a loving father

(3) Luke 15:11-32   (c) a woman searching

Pray. Thank God that He has made ways for you to know Him better.

15

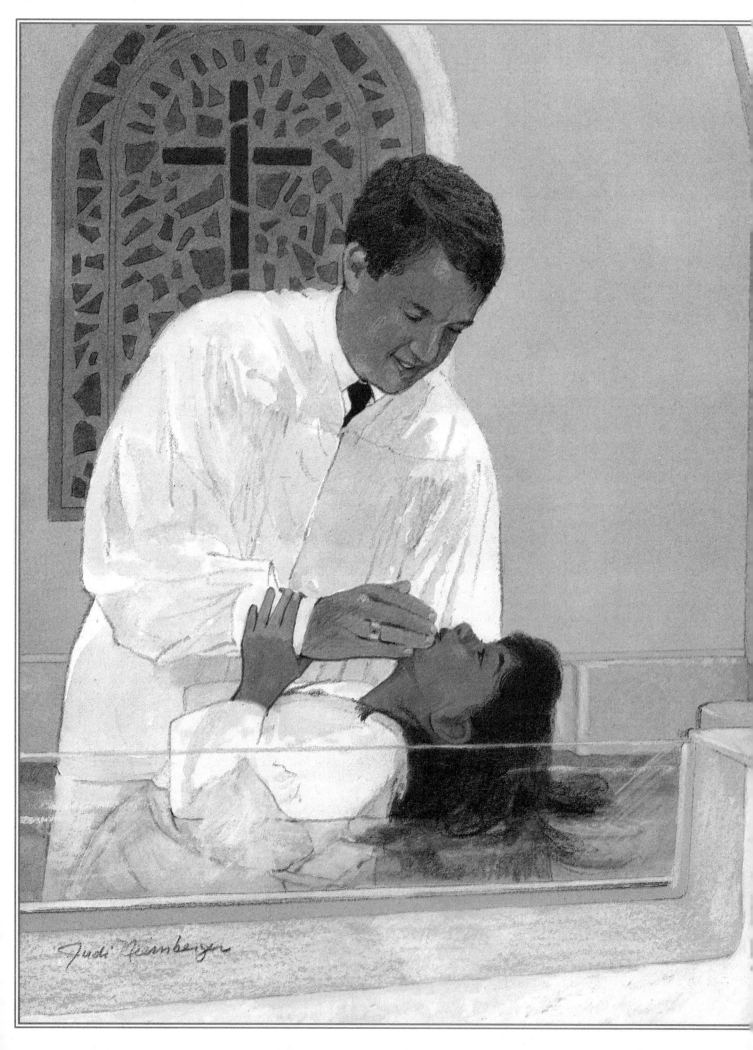

What Is a Church?

Bible verse: "[Paul wrote] Give my greetings to . . . the church in her house"
(Colossians 4:15).

What Is a New Testament Church?
A church is a group of baptized believers. They have chosen to do God's work together. A New Testament church tries to do things like the first churches. The New Testament, especially the Book of Acts, tells about these churches.

How Did the First Churches Begin?
When Jesus began his work on earth, He chose 12 disciples to help him. As Jesus went about teaching, others believed in Him.

When Jesus went to heaven, He left many followers. Many of these lived in Jerusalem. They joined together to tell others about Jesus. They became the first church.

What Was the First Church in Jerusalem Like?
These new Christians did not have a building to meet in. But they were still a church. They were persons who had trusted Jesus to save them. They joined together because they wanted to tell everyone what Jesus had done. They worshiped together. They tried to carry on Jesus' work. They tried to work and to solve their problems as God's Spirit taught them.

The New Testament is like a measuring stick for Christians and for churches. Check to see how your church measures up to the first church the New Testament tells about.

Find and read these verses in your Bible:

❏ Acts 2:41-47
List the things they did.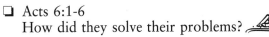

❏ Acts 6:1-6
How did they solve their problems?

❏ Acts 13:1-5
What were they doing when God's Spirit told them to send missionaries?

❏ 2 Corinthians 9:1-2,5
How did the people in Corinth feel about giving to others?

Pray. Thank God for churches.

17

What Work Do Churches Do?

> *Bible verse:* "Make disciples of all nations, baptizing them . . . and teaching them" *(Matthew 28:19-20).*

Reason for Starting the First Church

Jesus had a special reason for starting His church. He wanted His followers to do the work He did when He was on earth. When Jesus was on earth, He taught, preached, and helped people. He told His church to do the same.

Jesus did not mean that only missionaries are to do these things. He did not mean that only preachers are to do these things. He meant that every Christian should do His work.

The first churches did the work Jesus wanted them to do. When Jesus went back to heaven, He left more than 100 followers in Jerusalem. They began to tell people about Jesus. Soon the number of Christians had reached 5,000.

The Work Those New Church Members Did

- **They Witnessed.**
  Witness means to tell others what you know. Those early church members witnessed. That means they told other people about Jesus.

- **They Taught.**
  Jesus told the first church to teach.
  - All Christians need to keep learning what Jesus taught and did.
  - Each one needs to learn to pray.
  - Each one needs to study the Bible.
  - Each one needs to know how to do the work Jesus meant for His church to do.
  - Each one needs to know how Jesus wants him or her to live.

- **They Helped People in Need.**
  New Testament churches helped people in need.

Once there was a famine in Jerusalem. Other churches took up an offering. Members of those churches were also poor, but they found ways to give.

The churches also took care of widows and orphans. They remembered how Jesus helped persons who were sick, hungry, and disabled. Because they loved Jesus and one another, they cared about persons who were in need.

Think Time

Are you part of the church? _____

How can you witness? _____

_____

How can you learn about Jesus? _____

_____

How can you help people in need? _____

_____

Pray. Ask God to help your church be a caring church.

Baptism and the Lord's Supper

> *Bible verse:* "[The Philippian jailer] and all his family were baptized"
> *(Acts 16:33).*
> "Whenever you eat this bread and drink this cup, you proclaim the Lord's death
> until he comes" *(1 Corinthians 11:26).*

Why Did the First Churches Have Baptism and the Lord's Supper?

The first church wanted to remember Jesus just as Jesus had commanded them to remember Him. Jesus commanded Christians to remember Him in two ways—by baptism and the Lord's Supper.

How Do We Know Members of the First Churches Had Been Baptized?

The New Testament says so. One day three thousand people became Christians.

❑ Read Acts 2:41. What did the people do immediately?

_____

Always in New Testament churches the person baptized was already a believer in Jesus.

Why Did the First Church Baptize Christians?

They baptized because Jesus had set the example. Just before Jesus began His work on earth, He was baptized.

❑ Read Matthew 3:13-17. Who baptized Jesus?

_____

The first churches baptized for another reason. Jesus commanded it. Baptism is the way a Christian lets others know he has become a Christian.

❑ Read Matthew 28:19-20. What did Jesus say to do to those people who trusted Him?

_____

What Is Baptism?

Baptism is a picture. When a person is put under water, it is as if she is saying, "I have let Jesus bury my old way of living." When she is brought out of the water, she is saying, "I have begun a new life because of what Jesus has done for me."

Baptism is also a picture of Jesus–His death, burial, and resurrection. It reminds us of what Jesus has done for us.

Why Did the First Churches Eat the Lord's Supper?

The first church members observed the Lord's Supper because Jesus said, "Do this to remember me."

❑ Read 1 Corinthians 11:23-26. What command did Jesus give His disciples?

• _____ the bread

• drink from the _____.

❑ Read Acts 2:42. Did the church continue to observe this Supper in memory of Jesus?

_____

What Does the Lord's Supper Mean?

The first churches believed Jesus meant for His disciples to take the Lord's Supper to remember Him. When Christians take the Lord's Supper, they remember that Jesus died for them. The bread reminds them of Jesus' body which He gave on the cross. Drinking from the cup reminds a Christian of Jesus' blood which He shed on the cross.

Pray. Thank God for the meanings of baptism and the Lord's Supper.

19

How Should I Act During Baptism and the Lord's Supper?

Bible verse: "A man ought to examine himself before he eats of the bread and drinks of the cup" *(1 Corinthians 11:28).*

What Do You Do?

Think about your behavior during the observance of baptism and the Lord's Supper. The New Testament gives guidelines for Christians to use in observing the ordinances of baptism and the Lord's Supper. Read these Scripture passages. What do they say to you?

_____

_____

Draw lines to match the verses and statements.

1 Corinthians 11:23-26 •   • Tell about Jesus until He comes again.

1 Timothy 4:12 •   • Do things that cause others to praise God.

Matthew 5:16 •   • Be an example of God's way of living.

Stop and Think

Use these questions to help you think about what you can improve or change in your behavior when a person is baptized and when the Lord's Supper is served.

❏ Am I reverent?

❏ Do I disturb others by talking or moving around?

❏ Can others tell by my actions that I have accepted Jesus as my Savior?

❏ Do I use the observance of the ordinances (baptism and the Lord's Supper) as a time of worship?

❏ During the Lord's Supper do I remember what Jesus did for me, or do I try to get the biggest piece of bread and the glass with the most juice?

❏ When the pastor baptizes someone, do I really listen to what he says? Do I pray for the person?

❏ When a person is being baptized, do I think about the meaning of baptism?

❏ Do I tell others that I know Jesus by the way I behave during the Lord's Supper or when others are baptized?

How may God want me to change my behavior?

_____

_____

_____

Pray. Ask God to help you to be respectful during worship, baptism, and the Lord's Supper.

20

Think Back

> *Bible verse:* "Christ is the head of the church, his body, of which he is the Savior" *(Ephesians 5:23).*

Measure Your Church

- Does your church preach, telling persons about Jesus? How?

- Does your church baptize persons who have become Christians and who want to join your church?

- Does your church teach what Jesus taught? How?

- Does your church have fellowship together?

- What does *fellowship* mean? (Having parties or enjoying being together with other Christians?)

- Does your church observe the Lord's Supper? How?

- Does your church pray? When?

- Does your church share with one another and the needy? How?

- Does your church worship together? When?

- Does your church praise God? How? When?

- Does your church have a part in sending missionaries? How?

- What is a New Testament church?

Acts of a New Testament Church

- Preached
- Learned and taught
- Observed the Lord's Supper
- Shared
- Praised God
- Sent missionaries
- Baptized
- Had fellowship together
- Prayed
- Worshiped together
- Chose deacons for special duties
- Cooperated (worked with) other churches

Think About Answers to These Questions:

- What does baptism "say" to others?
- Who should be baptized?
- Why did Jesus begin the Lord's Supper?
- Why do churches today have the Lord's Supper?
- How should you act when your church observes the ordinances of baptism and the Lord's Supper?

Answer Yes (Y) or No (N)

___ Baptism is a way to confess publicly your faith in Jesus as your Savior.

___ Jesus started the Lord's Supper because He wanted His followers to remember Him.

Pray. Pray for the leaders of your church.

21

What Is Prayer?

Bible verse: "Pray continually" (1 Thessalonians 5:17).

Prayer Is Talking and Listening

Prayer has a special meaning for Christians. The story of the first Christians is found in the Book of Acts. Here are some of the first things that were written about them.

❑ Read Acts 1:14. This verse tells what Jesus' followers did after Jesus went back to heaven. They _____.

❑ Read Acts 1:24. This verse tells what Jesus' disciples did when they wanted to choose someone to take Judas' place. They _____.

❑ Read Acts 2:42. This verse tells what the first three thousand Christians did. They _____.

Prayer is *talking* and *listening* to God. The best place to find answers about prayer is from God. God speaks to people through the Bible. The Bible tells how to pray and why. The Bible contains many prayers people have prayed. Prayers that Jesus prayed are there.

But everything the Bible says about prayer does not begin: "Do this" or "Don't do this." Some things you learn from stories about real people and their prayers. You learn from stories Jesus told to help you understand what prayer is.

Read Luke 18:10-14. In this story Jesus told, one man looked as if he were praying. But he was only talking to himself. What do you think this story tells about prayer?

Place a check (✔) by the sentences that you think are true.

❑ Do not brag when you pray.

❑ When you pray, you are talking to God.

❑ Pray only so others can hear you.

Place a check (✔) by each of these reasons that you really believe is true.

❑ When you pray, you are near to God, and Christians need to stay near God.

❑ A Christian should pray because God commands His people to pray.

❑ Prayer helps a Christian make the right choices.

❑ Christians must have God's help if they want to act like Jesus.

God does not mean for you to go around with your eyes closed and your head bowed all the time. He does mean for you to remember that He is near at all times. He does want you to depend on–trust–Him and to thank Him.

Pray. Thank God for the Bible, your church, and people who teach you how to pray.

What Happens When I Pray?

> *Bible verse:* "Ask and it will be given to you; seek and you will find; knock and the door will be opened to you" *(Matthew 7:7).*

Decide what this true story tells about prayer.

Paul

I was first called Saul. I believed in the Jewish religion and hated all Jews who became Christians. I thought they were traitors to God and ought to be punished.

But one day I saw something that I could never forget. One of those Christians, whose name was Stephen, was dragged outside the city. He had been preaching that Jesus was God's Son. Angry men threw off their coats and tossed them at my feet. I watched as they stoned Stephen for being a Christian.

Just before he died, Stephen prayed. We could hear what he was praying. He asked God to forgive us for killing him.

Not long after this, something wonderful happened. It changed my whole life.

I was going to Damascus to arrest some Christians there. While on the road, a light from heaven came down and blinded me. Then Jesus asked me why I was persecuting Him.

While I was still blind, I prayed. While I prayed, God spoke to a Christian named Ananias. God told him to come help me. At first, he was afraid; he knew what I had been doing to other Christians. But because he believed and trusted God, Ananias came to me, and my blindness was taken away.

—Based on Acts 7:54 to 8:1; 9:1-18

Think Time

Christians ever since New Testament days have prayed, too. Ask someone you know who prays to tell you what happens when they pray. Write here what you hear them say.

_____

_____

_____

_____

My prayer list

Person   Prayer   God's Answer

Pray. Ask God to teach you to pray for people on your prayer list.

What Should I Pray About?

Bible verse: "The Lord has heard my cry for mercy; the Lord accepts my prayer" (Psalm 6:9).

The Model Prayer

A model is a plan or pattern for doing something. The disciples asked Jesus for a plan for praying. Jesus said:

> "This, then, is how you should pray: 'Our Father in heaven, hallowed be your name, your kingdom come, your will be done on earth as it is in heaven. Give us today our daily bread. Forgive us our debts, as we also have forgiven our debtors. And lead us not into temptation, but deliver us from the evil one'" (Matthew 6:9-13).

Many people think prayer is only asking for something you want. Someone has called these "gimme-prayers." But God plans for prayer to help Christians in more ways than this.

Pray to Give Thanks and Praise

Two words to know:
Praise is telling God how good and great He is. *Praise* is telling God how much you love Him.
Thanksgiving is telling God "thank You" for all the things He has done for you and for people you love.

Pray when you want to show thanks. Praying ought to start with praise and thanksgiving. Name some things you think you ought to thank God for. Why?

Pray for Courage and Strength

Pray when you need courage and strength. It is not easy to do the things God would have you do. That is what "your will be done" means. You need to pray for strength to be obedient.

Name some things you need God to help you to do. _____

_____

Pray for What You Need

Pray when you need "daily bread." Praying for our daily bread means you should not be greedy or selfish in your prayers.

Name some things you and your family need in order to live. _____

_____

_____

Name some things you want but do not need.

_____

_____

Pray for Forgiveness

Pray because you need forgiveness. Ask God to forgive you for anything you have done wrong during the day. Decide never to do a thing like that again. Also ask God to help you to forgive others.

Name some things that you have done that God needs to forgive you for. _____

_____

_____

Pray. Pray the model prayer as you read it.

25

How Do I Pray

> *Bible verse:* "Devote yourselves to prayer, being watchful and thankful"
> *(Colossians 4:2).*

The disciples knew they did not know how to pray as they should. They asked Jesus to teach them to pray (Luke 11:1).

What Words Should You Use When You Pray?
Speak to God as you would to a good friend.

What Way Should You Act When You Pray?
When you pray, should you stand, kneel, or sit? The Bible gives examples of people standing, kneeling, and even lying on their faces as they talked with God. People stood in prayer to show their respect for God. People knelt in prayer to ask God's forgiveness. They did not feel worthy of standing. Bowed heads and closed eyes help show respect and shut out things that could take our thoughts away from God.

You should show respect for God (be reverent). The position of your body is not as important as the desire in your heart to talk to God.

How Should You Feel When You Pray?
You should feel right toward God. But you should also feel right toward others when you pray. Jesus said we must forgive others because God has forgiven us already.

Where Should You Pray?
Many times you pray with others. Jesus spoke of going into a closet to pray. He meant it is good to get away from things which would keep you from thinking about God.

Christians who have regular prayer times alone are also ready to pray anywhere, anytime. They pray when they need God's help. They pray whenever and wherever they want to thank Him. And they also pray when they just want to talk to God.

Name some places you have prayed. _____

_____

_____

Draw a picture of the way that you are most comfortable praying.

Pray. Ask Jesus to teach you to pray.

Thinking Back

Bible verse: "This is the day the Lord has made; let us rejoice and be glad in it" *(Psalm 118:24).*

My Prayers

What problems about prayer do I need help with? If you need help in answering any of these questions, turn back through the material for the week and remember the days' materials that helped you most.

❏ When should I pray?

❏ Should I pray in a certain position?

❏ I do not know the right words. What words should I use?

❏ Where should I pray?

❏ I do not know what to say when I pray aloud.

The best way to learn to pray is to pray.

The best way to learn about prayer is to pray.

Kinds of Prayer

1. **Thank-you prayers (Thanksgiving)**
   "Give thanks to the Lord, for he is good; his love endures forever" *(Psalm 118:1).*

2. **Help-me prayers (Petition)**
   "Keep me safe, O God, for in you I take refuge" *(Psalm 16:1).*

3. **Help-others prayers (Intercession)**
   "[Jesus prayed] My prayer is not for them alone. I pray also for those who will believe in me through their message" *(John 17:20).*

4. **I-love-You prayers (Praise)**
   "Praise the Lord, O my soul. O Lord my God, you are very great" *(Psalm 104:1).*

5. **I-am-sorry prayers (Confession)**
   "For I know my transgressions, and my sin is always before me. Against you, you only, have I sinned" *(Psalm 51:3-4).*

Think Time

I thank You, God, for: _____

_____

_____

God, I want to ask You to: _____

_____

_____

I praise You, God, for: _____

_____

_____

Pray. Pray for your family and friends

Jesus Was Born

> *Bible verse:* "The angel said to them, 'Do not be afraid. I bring you good news of great joy that will be for all the people. Today in the town of David a Savior has been born to you; he is Christ the Lord'" *(Luke 2:10-11).*

For many years people longed for the coming of the Savior. Prophets told of His coming.

An angel told Mary that she would be the mother of the Savior. Mary was pledged to be married to Joseph.

Who told of Jesus' coming? _____

Mary and Joseph lived in Nazareth. The Old Testament said that Jesus would be born in Bethlehem.

The Romans liked to count the number of people who lived in their empire. To get a true count, the Romans asked people to go to the town in which they were born. Joseph's family came from Bethlehem.

Where was Joseph's family from? _____

Mary and Joseph traveled from the town of Nazareth to Bethlehem just in time for Jesus to be born there.

There was no room for them to stay in the inn. They stayed in a stable. That is where Jesus was born. Mary laid Jesus in a manger.

Check the correct boxes. Mary and Joseph . . .

❑ travel to Bethlehem.

❑ did not find room in the inn.

❑ had to stay in a stable.

Shepherds tending their sheep were frightened by an angel. The angel said, "Do not be afraid. I bring good news of great joy for all people. Today in the town of David a Savior has been born. He is Christ the Lord."

The shepherds went to Bethlehem. They found Mary and Joseph, and the baby, who was lying in a manger.

The shepherds went home, glorifying and praising God.

How did the shepherds feel when the angel first appeared to them? _____

How did the shepherds feel after the saw the baby? _____

Think Time
• How was Jesus' birth like yours?

• How was Jesus's birth different from yours?

Pray. Thank God that He sent Jesus to be your Savior.

29

Jesus Was Special

> *Bible verse:* "And being found in appearance as man, he humbled himself and became obedient to death–even death on a cross!" *(Philippians 2:8).*

A Special Baby

We learned Monday that Jesus' birth was a part of God's great plan for all people.

Jesus came to help people and tell them about God. God decided that Jesus should come to earth as a baby. Jesus would be born and grow up like other boys–but without sin.

Why did God decide to do this? Why should He become a baby on earth?

God Cares for People

All the time, God was helping people. But people could not see Him. They could not know how much He was helping them. God's Son became a baby so that He could grow up as people do.

Jesus helped people. He helped people by teaching them about God His Father. He helped sick people get well and blind people see. He helped a large, hungry crowd get something to eat.

List the different ways Jesus helped people.

_____

_____

_____

_____

_____

_____

Jesus Understands You

God knows what you do and what you think. This was true even before Jesus lived on earth. Because God's Son lived on earth, you *know* that God knows how a person feels. He knows how it feels to be hungry or thirsty. He knows how it feels to want things.

Jesus Helps You Understand God

The world is very big. You cannot understand how God ever made so many things. God cares for the things He has made.

Does God care for you? Jesus told us that He does. He helps you understand that God is near. God knows what you do. He sees what you need.

God will never forget about you. He hears you when you pray. He watches you as you play. Jesus told us so. Because Jesus said so, you can know it is true.

Make a prayer list of the things that made you feel sad or hurt you today. Does God know how you feel?

Pray. Thank God because He cares for everyone.

Jesus Is Our Savior

> *Bible verse:* "But God demonstrates his own love for us in this: While we were still sinners, Christ died for us" *(Romans 5:8)*.

What Lost Means

Going away from home can be fun. If you do not go too far, everything is all right. But what happens when you go too far? You may not know how to go back. Then, you are lost. Someone has to find you.

Why is it so bad to get lost from home? When you are lost, you are away from your family and friends. You need to be with people who love you. You are lonely. You are afraid. You feel bad. You may be in danger.

Jesus Came to Find Lost People

Being lost from God is like being lost from home. Only it is much sadder.

People need to belong to God. People need to love Him and listen to Him. People need to know that He loves them and cares for them. They need to want to please Him. They need to want to do what He wants them to do.

People choose their own way instead of God's. They want to please themselves instead of God. That makes people lost from God. Jesus came to earth to find this kind of lost people and to save them.

What Jesus Did for Lost People

Jesus knew that God had to punish wrong. Someone had to pay for our sins. And Jesus was the only One who could do that. He was the only One who had never done any wrong. So Jesus went to die. He did not die because He had done wrong. He died because He wanted to take our place–to save us. When Jesus died, He showed us how much God loves us.

Stop and read Isaiah 53:6.

• What are lost people like? _____

_____

• Who cares for the lost? _____

When a child is lost, parents often call 911. When you needed to find your way to God's love, who helped you learn about Jesus? _____

_____

Pray. Thank God that Jesus came to find and save lost people.

31

Jesus Wants You

Bible verse: "[Jesus] came to seek and to save what was lost" *(Luke 19:10)*.

God Loves You

It is important to know that God loves you. Sometimes, you forget about Him. God never forgets about you. Jesus helps you know that God wants to be your friend.

Whether you think about Him or not, God thinks about you. He always sees what you do. He even knows what you think. God does not watch you to punish you. He watches you because He loves you and wants you to be happy. He knows you can never really be happy disobeying Him. God even planned the way for you to be forgiven. And His plan cost Him the life of His only Son, Jesus.

God's Son came from heaven to earth. After He died, He rose from the dead. Then, He went to heaven to be with God.

You Have Decided to Follow Jesus

Jesus has done all that needs to be done to save you. Jesus is God the Son, who came to earth because He loves you. He shows you what God is like. He even died in your place.

But He did not decide for you. Only you could do that. Only you could decide to turn away from choosing your own way. Only you could decide to put your trust in Jesus and what He has done for you.

You Have Decided to Obey Jesus

Loving Jesus means wanting to do what Jesus wants you to do. It means deciding to let Him be in charge of your whole life.

Jesus wants you to have what is good. He does not want you to have what will hurt you or someone else. When you decided to trust your whole life to Jesus that meant deciding that you no longer would choose to do what you want to. You decided to let Jesus help you know what to do.

When you play follow-the-leader, you act exactly like the leader. When you follow Jesus, what do you do? _____

_____

List ways you are choosing to follow Jesus.

_____

_____

_____

_____

_____

Pray. Thank God for the people who helped you know how to be saved.

Looking Back

Bible verse: "For the wages of sin is death, but the gift of God is eternal life in Christ Jesus our Lord" *(Romans 6:23).*

What Does It Mean to Accept Jesus as Lord?

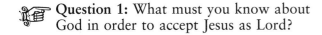 **Question 1:** What must you know about God in order to accept Jesus as Lord?

Answer: No one can see God. Sometimes God seems close. Sometimes you forget about God. But Jesus said that God never forgets about you. Jesus helps you know God wants to be your friend.

God always sees what you do. He even knows what you think. God does not watch you to catch and punish you. He watches you because He loves you and wants you to be happy. He knows that you can never really be happy disobeying Him. God even planned the way for each person to be forgiven. And this plan cost God the life of His only Son.

Question 2: What has Jesus done to deserve being called Lord?

Answer: Jesus made the way for each person to be friends with God forever. Leading you to be a friend with God is more than showing you how to do good deeds. It is making sure you are forgiven for disobeying God.

Jesus came from heaven to earth. Here He lived as a man in every way but one: Jesus never sinned. He never chose His own way. Yet He died to take the punishment for all the sin of all people of all times.

Each person can trust Jesus for forgiveness. He deserves your trust because of what He did for you. He deserves to be Lord, your Ruler and Master.

Question 3: If Jesus has done so much, is there anything a person has to do in order for Jesus to be his Savior?

Answer: Each person must decide. You must decide for yourself to trust Jesus. You must decide whether to turn away from choosing your own way. You must decide to put your trust in Jesus. Jesus has done all that needs to be done so that you can be forgiven by God. Jesus died in your place.

When you decided to trust Jesus, you decided to trust Him to save you.

Question 4: What do I do after I trust Jesus to save me?

Answer: You do all you can to obey Jesus' commands.

When a person really loves someone else, he wants to do what will please the one he loves. A person who loves and trusts Jesus will want to do what Jesus wants him to do.

Jesus wants His followers to have what is good. He does not want them to have what will hurt them or others. Trusting Jesus as Lord means you let Jesus help you know what is right to do.

Pray. Thank Jesus for saving you.

33

What Does the Bible Say about Witnesssing

> *Bible verse:* "That if you confess with your mouth, 'Jesus is Lord,' and believe in your heart that God raised him from the dead, you will be saved" *(Romans 10:9).*

The Bible teaches that a person who has given his life to Jesus should "confess Jesus before men."

Profession of Faith

To confess Jesus means to tell someone about Jesus. A new Christian wants to tell people in his church that he has become a Christian. This is called his "profession of faith" to the church. This is the first sharing of faith that many Christians do.

In many churches an invitation hymn is sung at the end of most worship services. During the singing of the hymn people can walk down the aisle and tell the preacher about choices they have made about Jesus. *Going forward during* an invitation is a way to say "I have trusted in Jesus to save me."

Baptism

Baptism is another way a believer (one who has trusted Jesus as his Savior) tells that he is a Christian. Baptism is like saying to everyone, "I want you to know what Jesus has done for me."

Lord's Supper

Taking the Lord's Supper is another way to tell others about Jesus. The Lord's Supper is a way to say: "I am a Christian. Jesus died for me. Jesus arose from the grave. Jesus will come again." Paul wrote, "For whenever you eat this bread and drink this cup, you proclaim the Lord's death until he comes" (1 Corinthians 11:26).

Think Time

Check (✔) the things you have done that told others that you are a Christian.

❏ I have made a profession of faith.

❏ I have been baptized.

❏ I take the Lord's Supper.

❏ I ask people to come to church.

❏ I tell others about Jesus.

Pray. Ask God to help you become a better witness.

35

Christians Tell about Jesus by the Way They Live

> *Bible verse:* "Let your light shine before men, that they may see your good deeds and praise your Father in heaven" (*Matthew 5:16*).

Forgiving

Christians tell others about Jesus by *forgiving.* Jesus set the example for forgiving. When He was on the cross, He asked God to forgive the people who had crucified Him (Luke 23:34). There may be times when a Christian feels that others have not been fair to him. Forgiving is never easy. But forgiving is one way to share God's love.

Being Kind

Christians tell about Jesus by *being kind.* Jesus did not pick out special people to be kind to. Others did, not Jesus. Once a crowd of good people gathered around a woman. They thought they were good. They were not as bad as she was. Even the law said they could throw stones at her. But Jesus said, "Any one of you who has never done anything wrong has the right to throw the first stone." He spoke kindly to the woman. No one dared to throw a stone. Read Matthew 5:43-48.

How are we to treat our enemies? _____

_____

Sharing

Christians tell by *sharing.* One day Jesus and His disciples needed to go to a quiet place to rest. But the people did not want Jesus to leave. They wanted to be with Him. They listened to Jesus talk. When it was time to eat, the disciples wanted to send the people home. Jesus wanted to feed them. A boy had brought five loaves and two fishes. He gave them to Jesus who broke them into pieces. The hungry people were fed. A boy learned what Jesus could do when one of His followers was willing to share what he had. Read 2 Corinthians 9:7.

How does God want us to share?_____

_____

Draw a picture of a time when you have . . .

Forgiven someone even though he hurt you.

Been kind to someone.

Shared something with someone.

Pray. Ask God to help you live for Jesus every day.

36

What Is the Message Christians Are to Tell All People?

> *Bible verse:* "Christ died for our sins according to the Scriptures, that he was buried, that he was raised on the third day according to the Scriptures" *(1 Corinthians 15:3-4).*

The message Christians tell is the story of Jesus. Jesus came–as a part of God's great and good plan for people.

☞ Jesus was born in the little town of Bethlehem. Out on the hillside shepherds watched over their sheep. Suddenly, the shepherds were in the middle of a bright light. An angel said to them: "Do not be afraid. I have good news. The Savior was born today in Bethlehem."

The shepherds went to Bethlehem. They saw Jesus–God's great love gift. God had sent His only Son to earth. Jesus would save people from sin.

☞ As people saw Jesus, they thought of God. Jesus made known what God is like by the way He lived, by what He said, and by what He did.

☞ Not all people who heard Jesus liked what He said or did. Some people did not believe He was the Son of God. They nailed Jesus to a cross. But Jesus prayed for people. "Father, forgive them," Jesus prayed, "for they do not know what they are doing." They were killing God's Son. And He was the Savior men had been looking for since Adam and Eve were the first to rebel against God.

Finally, Jesus said, "It is finished." His work was done. He died because of sin–not His, but ours.

☞ Friends of Jesus buried Him in a borrowed tomb. Early in the morning some women came to the tomb. To their surprise, the stone was rolled away. The tomb was empty!

The angel of the Lord said, "Do not be afraid. He is not here. He is risen."

The women hurried to tell the disciples the good news.

Jesus lives. The disciples and other followers saw Jesus many times after He arose. Five hundred saw Him at one time. Once He appeared to some of the disciples as they were fishing early in the morning. Another time He gave a command to the eleven disciples. Read Matthew 28:19-20.

☞ After 40 days Jesus took His followers to a hill near Jerusalem. There He told them to go everywhere, telling people about Him.

☞ After that, Jesus was lifted up from the ground into the sky. At last the disciples could see Him no longer.

Then two angels appeared and said: "Jesus is gone into heaven. But He will come again, just as He went."

Think Time
Practice telling the story of Jesus in your own words.

Pray. Thank God for the message about Jesus.

Christians Can Pray for Lost People

> *Bible verse:* "I [Paul] urge . . . prayers . . . be made for everyone"
> *(1 Timothy 2:1).*

There are times when you cannot speak up for Jesus. There are places where you cannot easily tell others about Jesus. At times and places like that you can live like a Christian–and you can pray.

Some Christians make a list of the names of people who are not Christians. They pray for these people each day. Do you know persons who are not Christians? Have you told them about your be-coming a Christian? Do you pray that they, too, will come to know Jesus as their Lord and Savior?

Remember, prayer is talking with God. You can pray often and thank God for His help. You can pray for people who have needs. You can pray for government leaders. You can pray for missionaries and church leaders. You can pray for the salvation of others.

People Who Need to Know Jesus

Names of people	Have you told them about Jesus?	Are you praying for them?

People Who Have Other Needs

Names of people	Needs they have	Answers to your prayer

Pray. Pray for one person you know who needs to know Jesus.

38

Looking Back

> *Bible verse:* "[Jesus said] You will receive power when the Holy Spirit comes on you; and you will be my witnesses" *(Acts 1:8).*

This week you have thought about the importance of telling others about Jesus. You also have thought about the story or message you want to tell. Now as you think back, think about your own testimony–the story of how you were saved. Here are some ideas that many people use when they give their testimonies.

My Life Before I Became a Christian
Check the sentences that describe your thoughts and feelings. Add you own words.

❏ I wanted to please myself more than I wanted to please God.

❏ Something was not right between God and me.

I Came to Know that I Needed Jesus to Save Me
❏ I knew my sin was against God.

❏ I was not right with God.

❏ I wanted to make things right with God.

❏ I wanted to go to heaven.

❏ I needed Jesus to save me.

❏ Jesus did not force me to trust in Him to save me.

How I Became a Christian
❏ I knew I was not right with God.

❏ I learned that I could not save or change myself.

❏ I learned that Jesus did all that is needed for me to be saved.

❏ I prayed for Jesus to forgive me of my sin.

❏ I trusted Jesus to save me and asked Him to be my Savior.

How Jesus Helps Me to Live for Him
❏ I am tempted or drawn to doing wrong, but Jesus helps me do right.

❏ Jesus helps me live for Him.

❏ I know that I am not perfect; I still sin. But now I am deeply sorry for my sin and ask forgiveness. I am no longer happy living in ways that do not please God.

Now share your testimony by telling someone what Jesus means to you.

Pray. Ask God to help you pray for others and to tell them about Jesus.

39

CERTIFICATE

This certificate is awarded to

_____

in recognition of the completion of the study of *Now That I'm a Christian*

_____ _____
church   city

_____
state

_____ _____
adult helper   pastor

Date I began work in *Now That I'm a Christian* _____